Tomie dePaola's

THE THREE LITTLE KITTENS

and other poems and songs
from Mother Goose

LITTLE
MAMMOTH

This ediiton first published
in Great Britain in 1987
by Magnet Paperbacks
Reissued 1989 as a Little Mammoth
an imprint of Mandarin Paperbacks
Michelin House,
81 Fulham Road,
London SW3 6RB
Taken from Tomie de Paola's MOTHER GOOSE
first published in 1985 by Methuen Children's Books.
Illustrations copyright © 1985 by Tomie de paola
Wherever possible, the MOTHER Goose rhymes
in this book are classic versions collected by
Peter and Ioan Opie.

Produced by Mandarin Offset
Printed and bound in Hong Kong

ISBN 0 7497 0097 1

I love little pussy,
    Her coat is so warm,
And if I don't hurt her
    She'll do me no harm.
So I'll not pull her tail,
    Nor drive her away,
But pussy and I
    Very gently will play.
She shall sit by my side,
    And I'll give her some food;
And pussy will love me
    Because I am good.

Puss came dancing out of a barn
With a pair of bagpipes under her arm;
She could sing nothing, but, Fiddle cum fee,
The mouse has married the humble-bee.
Pipe, cat—dance, mouse—
We'll have a wedding at our good house.

Oh where, oh where has my little dog gone?
Oh where, oh where can he be?
With his ears cut short and his tail cut long,
Oh where, oh where is he?

Sing, sing,
What shall I sing?
The cat's run away
With the pudding string!

Do, do,
What shall I do?
The cat's run away
With the pudding too!

Little Blue Ben, who lives in the glen,
Keeps a blue cat and one blue hen,
Which lays of blue eggs a score and ten;
Where shall I find the little Blue Ben?

Three young rats with black felt hats,
Three young ducks with white straw flats,
Three young dogs with curling tails,
Three young cats with demi-veils,
Went out to walk with two young pigs
In satin vests and sorrel wigs;
But suddenly it chanced to rain
And so they all went home again.

Three little kittens
They lost their mittens,
    And they began to cry,
Oh, Mother dear,
We sadly fear
    Our mittens we have lost.
What! lost your mittens,
You naughty kittens!
    Then you shall have no pie.
    Mee-ow, mee-ow, mee-ow.
    No, you shall have no pie.

The three little kittens
They found their mittens,
    And they began to cry,
Oh, Mother dear,
See here, see here,
    Our mittens we have found.
Put on your mittens,
You silly kittens,
    And you shall have some pie.
    Purr-r, purr-r, purr-r,
    Oh, let us have some pie.

The three little kittens
Put on their mittens
    And soon ate up the pie;
Oh, Mother dear,
We greatly fear
    Our mittens we have soiled.
What! soiled your mittens,
You naughty kittens!
    Then they began to sigh,
    Mee-ow, mee-ow, mee-ow,
    Then they began to sigh.

The three little kittens
They washed their mittens,
   And hung them out to dry;
Oh, Mother dear,
Do you not hear,
   Our mittens we have washed.
What! washed your mittens,
Then you're good kittens,
   But I smell a rat close by.
   Mee-ow, mee-ow, mee-ow,
   We smell a rat close by.

High diddle doubt, my candle's out
My little maid is not at home;
Saddle my hog and bridle my dog,
And fetch my little maid home.

Pussy cat, pussy cat,
    Where have you been?
I've been to London
    To look at the Queen.
Pussy cat, pussy cat,
    What did you there?
I frightened a little mouse
    Under her chair.

"I went up one pair of stairs."
  "Just like me."
"I went up two pairs of stairs."
  "Just like me."
"I went into a room."
  "Just like me."
"I looked out of a window."
  "Just like me."
"And there I saw a monkey."
  "Just like me."

Three blind mice, see how they run!
They all ran after the farmer's wife,
Who cut off their tails with a carving knife,
Did you ever see such a thing in your life,
  As three blind mice?

I had a little hen,
   The prettiest ever seen;
She washed up the dishes,
   And kept the house clean.
She went to the mill
   To fetch me some flour,
And always got home
   In less than an hour.
She baked me my bread,
   She brewed me my ale,
She sat by the fire
   And told a fine tale.

I had a cat and the cat pleased me,
I fed my cat by yonder tree;
Cat goes fiddle-i-fee.

I had a hen and the hen pleased me,
I fed my hen by yonder tree;
Hen goes chimmy-chuck, chimmy-chuck,
Cat goes fiddle-i-fee.

I had a duck and the duck pleased me,
I fed my duck by yonder tree;
    Duck goes quack, quack,
    Hen goes chimmy-chuck, chimmy-chuck,
    Cat goes fiddle-i-fee.

I had a goose and the goose pleased me,
I fed my goose by yonder tree;
    Goose goes swishy, swashy,
    Duck goes quack, quack,
    Hen goes chimmy-chuck, chimmy-chuck,
    Cat goes fiddle-i-fee.

I had a sheep and the sheep pleased me,
I fed my sheep by yonder tree;
    Sheep goes baa, baa,
    Goose goes swishy, swashy,
    Duck goes quack, quack,
    Hen goes chimmy-chuck, chimmy-chuck,
    Cat goes fiddle-i-fee.

I had a pig and the pig pleased me,
I fed my pig by yonder tree;
    Pig goes griffy, gruffy,
    Sheep goes baa, baa,
    Goose goes swishy, swashy,
    Duck goes quack, quack,
    Hen goes chimmy-chuck, chimmy-chuck,
    Cat goes fiddle-i-fee.

I had a cow and the cow pleased me,
I fed my cow by yonder tree;
    Cow goes moo, moo,
    Pig goes griffy, gruffy,
    Sheep goes baa, baa,
    Goose goes swishy, swashy,
    Duck goes quack, quack,
    Hen goes chimmy-chuck, chimmy-chuck,
    Cat goes fiddle-i-fee.

I had a horse and the horse pleased me,
I fed my horse by yonder tree;
    Horse goes neigh, neigh,
    Cow goes moo, moo,
    Pig goes griffy, gruffy,
    Sheep goes baa, baa,
    Goose goes swishy, swashy,
    Duck goes quack, quack,
    Hen goes chimmy-chuck, chimmy-chuck,
    Cat goes fiddle-i-fee.

I had a dog and the dog pleased me,
I fed my dog by yonder tree;
    Dog goes bow-wow, bow-wow,
    Horse goes neigh, neigh,
    Cow goes moo, moo,
    Pig goes griffy, gruffy,
    Sheep goes baa, baa,
    Goose goes swishy, swashy,
    Duck goes quack, quack,
    Hen goes chimmy-chuck, chimmy-chuck,
    Cat goes fiddle-i-fee.

A wise old owl sat in an oak,
The more he heard the less he spoke;
The less he spoke the more he heard.
Why aren't we all like that wise old bird?

Goosey, goosey gander,
  Whither shall I wander?
Upstairs and downstairs
  And in my lady's chamber.
There I met an old man
  Who would not say his prayers,
I took him by the left leg
  And threw him down the stairs.

Chook, chook, chook, chook, chook,
  Good morning, Mrs. Hen.
How many chickens have you got?
  Madam, I've got ten.
Four of them are yellow,
  And four of them are brown,
And two of them are speckled red,
  The nicest in the town.

Dame Trot and her cat
  Sat down for a chat;
The Dame sat on this side
  And puss sat on that.

Puss, says the Dame,
  Can you catch a rat,
Or a mouse in the dark?
  Purr, says the cat.

Ladybird, ladybird,
　　Fly away home,
Your house is on fire
　　And your children all gone;
All except one
　　And that's little Ann
And she has crept under
　　The warming pan.

On the first of March,
The crows begin to search;
By the first of April
They are sitting still;
By the first of May
They've all flown away,
Coming greedy back again
With October's wind and rain.

Hickety, pickety, my black hen,
She lays eggs for gentlemen;
Gentlemen come every day
To see what my black hen doth lay.

Little Poll Parrot
  Sat in his garret
Eating toast and tea;
  A little brown mouse
    Jumped into the house
And stole it all away.

First in a carriage,
Second in a gig,
Third on a donkey,
And fourth on a pig.

Great A, little a,
Bouncing B,
The cat's in the cupboard
And can't see me.

Dickery, dickery, dare,
The pig flew up in the air;
The man in brown
Soon brought him down,
Dickery, dickery, dare.

The lion and the unicorn
    Were fighting for the crown;
The lion beat the unicorn
    All around the town.

Some gave them white bread,
    And some gave them brown;
Some gave them plum cake
    And drummed them out of town.